This Bucket List Journal Belongs To:

____

My Bucket List

Bucket List

What

Why

How

Completed

Date

Where

With

Notes/Thoughts/Memories

Would I Do It Again?

yes

no

Memories In Pictures

Souvenirs

Bucket List

What

Why

How

Completed

Date

Where

With

Notes/Thoughts/Memories

yes

no

Would I Do It Again?

Memories In Pictures

Souvenirs

Bucket List

What

Why

How

Completed

Date

Where

With

Notes/Thoughts/Memories

yes

no

Would I Do It Again?

Memories In Pictures

Souvenirs

Bucket List

What

Why

How

Completed

Date

Where

With

Notes/Thoughts/Memories

Would I Do It Again? yes ☐ no ☐

Memories In Pictures

Souvenirs

Bucket List

What

Why

How

Completed

Date

Where

With

Notes/Thoughts/Memories

Would I Do It Again?

yes

no

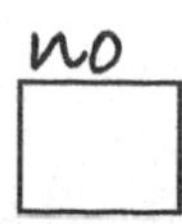

Memories In Pictures

Souvenirs

Bucket List

What

Why

How

Completed

Date

Where

With

Notes/Thoughts/Memories

yes

no

Would I Do It Again?

Memories In Pictures

Souvenirs

Bucket List

What

Why

How

Completed

Date

Where

With

Notes/Thoughts/Memories

Would I Do It Again?

yes

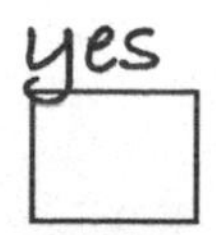

no

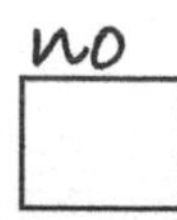

Memories In Pictures

Souvenirs

Bucket List

What

Why

How

Completed

Date

Where

With

Notes/Thoughts/Memories

Would I Do It Again? yes ☐ no ☐

Memories In Pictures

Souvenirs

Bucket List

What

Why

How

Completed

Date

Where

With

Notes/Thoughts/Memories

Would I Do It Again?

yes

no

Memories In Pictures

Souvenirs

Bucket List

What

Why

How

Completed

Date

Where

With

Notes/Thoughts/Memories

Would I Do It Again? yes ☐ no ☐

Memories In Pictures

Souvenirs

Bucket List

What

Why

How

Completed

Date

Where

With

Notes/Thoughts/Memories

Would I Do It Again?

yes

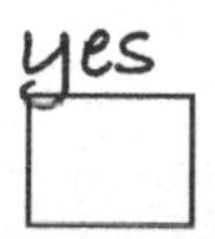

no

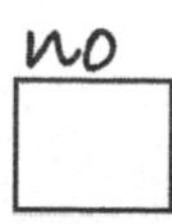

Memories In Pictures

Souvenirs

Bucket List

What

Why

How

Completed

Date

Where

With

Notes/Thoughts/Memories

Would I Do It Again? yes ☐ no ☐

Memories In Pictures

Souvenirs

Bucket List

What

Why

How

Completed

Date

Where

With

Notes/Thoughts/Memories

Would I Do It Again?

yes

no

Memories In Pictures

Souvenirs

Bucket List

What

Why

How

Completed

Date

Where

With

Notes/Thoughts/Memories

Would I Do It Again? yes ☐ no ☐

Memories In Pictures

Souvenirs

Bucket List

What

Why

How

Completed

Date

Where

With

Notes/Thoughts/Memories

yes

no

Would I Do It Again?  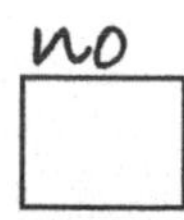

Memories In Pictures

Souvenirs

Bucket List

What

Why

How

Completed

Date

Where

With

Notes/Thoughts/Memories

Would I Do It Again? yes ☐ no ☐

Memories In Pictures

Souvenirs

Bucket List

What

Why

How

Completed

Date

Where

With

Notes/Thoughts/Memories

Would I Do It Again?

yes

no

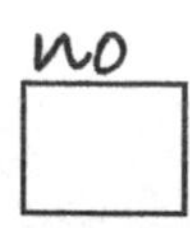

Memories In Pictures

Souvenirs

Bucket List

What

Why

How

Completed

Date

Where

With

Notes/Thoughts/Memories

Would I Do It Again? yes ☐ no ☐

Memories In Pictures

Souvenirs

Bucket List

What

Why

How

Completed

Date

Where

With

Notes/Thoughts/Memories

Would I Do It Again?

yes

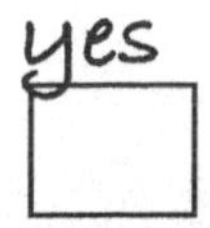

no

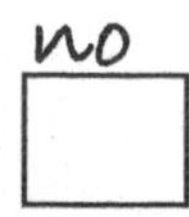

Memories In Pictures

Souvenirs

Bucket List

What

Why

How

Completed

Date

Where

With

Notes/Thoughts/Memories

Would I Do It Again? yes ☐ no ☐

Memories In Pictures

Souvenirs

Bucket List

What

Why

How

Completed

Date

Where

With

Notes/Thoughts/Memories

Would I Do It Again?

yes

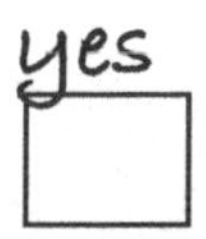

no

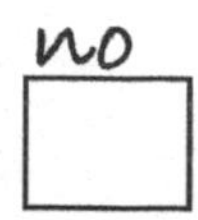

Memories In Pictures

Souvenirs

Bucket List

What

Why

How

Completed

Date

Where

With

Notes/Thoughts/Memories

Would I Do It Again? yes ☐ no ☐

Memories In Pictures

Souvenirs

Bucket List

What

Why

How

Completed

Date

Where

With

Notes/Thoughts/Memories

yes

no

Would I Do It Again? 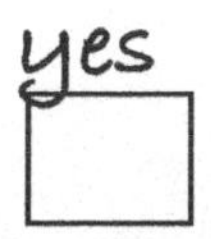 

Memories In Pictures

Souvenirs

Journal

Journal

Journal

Journal

Journal

Journal

Journal

Journal

Journal

Journal

Journal

Journal

Journal

Journal

Journal

Journal

Journal

Journal

Journal

Journal

Journal

Journal

Journal

Journal

Journal

Journal

Journal

Journal

Journal

Journal

Journal

Journal

Journal

Journal

Journal

Journal

Journal

Journal

Journal

Made in the USA
Coppell, TX
14 February 2023

12756359R10069